If your name **isn't**

MILES MORALES

then close this **journal!**

P.S. I'm serious!

SPIDER-MAN: INTO THE SPIDER-VERSE: THE JOURNAL

A CENTUM BOOK 978-1-912707-45-4

Published in Great Britain by Centum Books Ltd

This edition published 2018

1 3 5 7 9 10 8 6 4 2

MARVEL

© 2018 MARVEL © 2018 SPA & CPII

Centum Books Ltd, 20 Devon Square, Newton Abbot, Devon, TQ12 2HR, UK

books@centumbooksltd.co.uk

CENTUM BOOKS Limited Reg. No. 07641486

A CIP catalogue record for this book is available from the British Library

Printed in Poland.

SPIDER-MAN
INTO THE SPIDER-VERSE

THE JOURNAL

ALERT!

Mum, Dad – if you're STILL reading this, even after the big warnings on the first page, then

STOP!

This is MY journal!

It's just going be a load of boring science stuff.

Y'know, page after page of Multiverse Theory and what it means...

Hey!

Okay, so it's been a wild time.
I think if I write down some of my thoughts, hopefully it'll help me to get a handle on things.

I wasn't joking when I said that I loved science and Multiverse Theory and all that stuff. I do. But lately, I kind of have some other interests. Well, ONE other interest.

Have you ever heard of Spider-Man?

Of course you have.

Well, funny thing...

I AM Spider-Man.

Well, one of 'em, anyway.

Confusing?

Yeah, I know how it feels. But stick with me and we'll work it out.

This is my family.

Dad
(Jefferson)

Uncle Aaron
(uh, Uncle Aaron)

Mum
(Rio)

Me
(Miles, obvs)

Now, I ♡love♡ my parents.

My mum is cool and my dad is ... well, he's cool, I guess.

But he's a police officer.

He's a 'by the book' kind of guy.
And he sort of doesn't like Spider-Man.
The original one.

Oh yeah, and Uncle Aaron, I almost forgot about him.
He's my dad's brother. I like him a lot, but according
to my parents he's kind of a bad influence.

Y'know, 'cause he likes to have FUN.

Wait, that's confusing, too. Well, I'll try to explain it later.

Here I am in class!

Learning!
Getting smart(er)!

I was a little nervous about switching schools
(did I mention that I used to go to Brooklyn Middle School?)
and sometimes, if I'm being truthful,
I'd like to go back.

But Brooklyn Visions Academy ...

WOW!

The teachers there are amazing
and I can really learn a lot.

I really miss my old friends, though.
Maybe if I give these new kids a chance...?

SPIDEY

MORALES

One major downside to BVA – the homework.

There's a tonne of it.

Not that we didn't have a lot at Brooklyn Middle.

But I swear Visions hands out homework by the truckload.

So here's a pic of me, slogging through maths or whatever,

and that's Ganke.

I'll write more about him later.

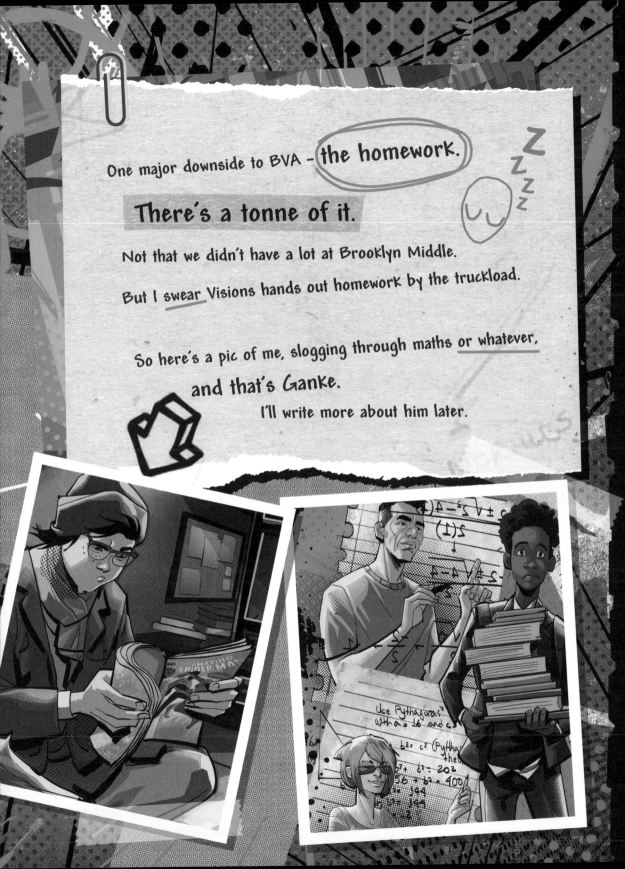

Remember how I mentioned that my parents don't like me hanging out with Uncle Aaron?

Yeah, well, take a look at this pic.

This is probably what they're talking about.

L.O.L

We **don't** go out and get into **trouble** or anything, but Uncle Aaron sort of encourages me to head out and

express myself.

After we've climbed a really tall fence.

This is what I'm talking about!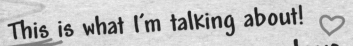

I love science and all, but I also **love** making art.

I'll sketch things up during the day, then go out at night with my Uncle Aaron to make these works of art on the subway walls.

Uncle Aaron says that my dad used to take him down here when they were younger.

Before he became a cop.

I like hanging out with Uncle Aaron, because I can actually forget about everything else and just concentrate on art.

It helps keep me focused.

Except for that one time when I went down there and got bitten by this weird glowing spider.

That kind of unfocused everything really quickly.

So that's my life in a nutshell.

I have good parents,

go to a new school

that's NOT my old school,

have a ... roommate

and I got bitten by a spider.

That gave me powers.

Friends and Family

I talked a little about my mum and dad, and I sort of mentioned Ganke already. But I want to write more about them. I'll do that over the next few pages, so keep on reading!

DAD

MUM

MORALES

UNCLE AARON

GANKE

WANDA

So, yeah, Mum and Dad.
Rio and Jefferson.

Not that I'd ever call them that to their faces – not unless I felt like never leaving the house again for the rest of my life.

MUM

My mum <u>always</u> has my back and I think we really get each other. At least, I feel like she gets me.

DAD

But my dad? Well ... I know he wants what's best for me and I know he loves me, but ... <u>he's just really hard on me.</u> Maybe one day things will be better between us.

Here's a selfie of me with Aaron Morales, my dad's brother and my uncle.

LEGEND.

My dad is always saying stuff to me like,

"You don't want to end up like your Uncle Aaron, do you?"

or,

"We all make choices in life, Miles – don't make choices like your Uncle Aaron!"

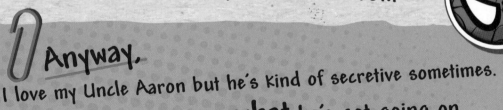

Anyway,

I love my Uncle Aaron but he's kind of secretive sometimes.

Like, I don't know **what** he's got going on.

But there's **something.**

I really **loved** going to Brooklyn Middle School.

I had it **all worked out**, you know?

I could ace any test, breeze through my homework and I had lots of friends.

They all miss me, now that I'm going to Visions.

They also like to give me a hard time, making fun of my school uniform.

I tell them that **Visions makes me wear it**, it's not my idea of fashion.

Not that I'm sure I really have any idea about fashion.

I grew up in a really great neighbourhood.

Everyone knows everybody and we're all pretty friendly with each other.

One of my neighbours, Herschel? He says **"hi"**

to me every time I walk past his place.

"Buenas dias, Miles!"

Herschel says he likes to greet me that way
because my mum is from Puerto Rico.

Which is pretty cool of him,
even though I'm from Brooklyn.

The guy gets an 'A' for effort!

GANKE   ME

Ganke is my roommate at Visions.

For the first couple of weeks, I wasn't sure if Ganke could talk or not.

All I knew about him was, he went to class, did his homework and he liked to read Spider-Man comics with his headphones on.

But after a little while, we warmed up to each othe

And then there's Wanda.

At least, she says her name is Wanda. Because when I first met her,

she told me her name was Gwanda. **With a 'G'.**

And that she was South African, but raised in the States which is why she didn't have an accent. Turns out she was just messing with me.

That's how you start a beautiful friendship!

WANDA A.K.A. GWANDA

Yeah right!

Okay, embarrassing story.

So I mentioned that I got bitten by that spider, right? And I got powers, right? Well, at first I didn't know what they were or how to control them or anything.

So when I met Wanda and I sort of touched her shoulder, I stuck to her. Like, REALLY stuck to her.

The more I tried to get unstuck, the more stuck I got and then pretty soon her hair was involved. The school nurse had to shave her hair just to separate us.

EMBARRASSING.

U

Another, (slightly) less embarrassing story?

So I sort of sneaked out of Visions Academy one night after I first got there, to go and see my Uncle Aaron.

I thought nobody saw me. **I thought <u>wrong.</u>**

The security guard, whose name is ...

WOW, you know, I don't know what his name is.

Anyway. Ooops

He saw me the next day and ran after me.
I tried to lose him and accidentally ran into his office.

That was a hot mess.

To be continued...

MILES MORALES

Made it in the end!

So, other than a **few** embarrassing incidents, I'm a pretty lucky kid.

Lucky,
because I have people in my life who really care about me.

And who like to wear headphones and read Spider-Man comic books, or tell me that their name is really Gwanda.

Brooklyn Visions Academy

My new school!

I'm **still** trying to work out where everything is, who everybody is and ... **well, everything!**

It's a big place, a lot bigger than Brooklyn Middle School.

A person could easily get lost. **Let's hope I don't!***

*I DEFINITELY WILL.

I remember the **first time** I walked into the reception of Visions Academy. **Everyone** seemed **taller** than me and all I could see were

blue uniforms everywhere.

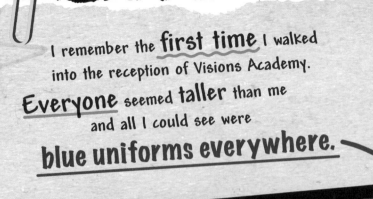

At first, I thought the place was kind of elitist – y'know,
I just wanted to go back to Brooklyn Middle with my **normal** friends,
instead of a bunch of **over-achieving brainiacs.**
But Mum and Dad (especially Dad)
wanted me to go here.

It **wasn't easy** getting into Visions Academy.

First, you had to win a lottery to even be considered for a spot.

Then, you had to take an **entrance exam.**

Well, not just take it, you had to **pass it.**

Well, **not just** pass it, you had to **totally ace it.**

I totally aced it.

It's an incredible school,
backed by a lot of big-money types
like **Wilson Fisk** and **Alchemax Laboratories.**

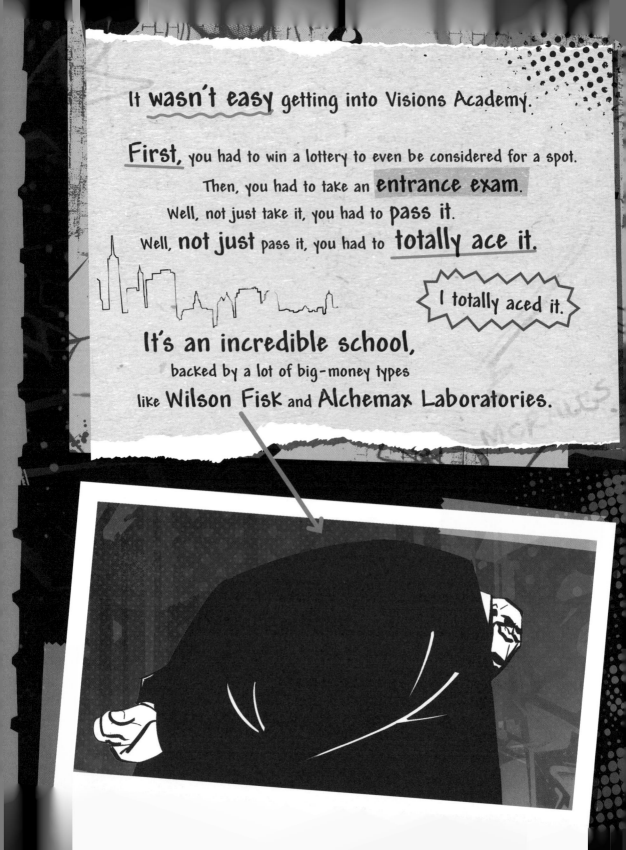

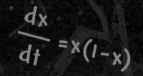

This is Ms Calleros, one of my teachers.

PHYSICS.

She's **super-smart** and **super-intimidating**, and I'm always **super-late** to her class. I had to write down this conversation we had the other day, because I thought it was funny:

L.O.L.

Ms CALLEROS: You're late, Mr Morales.

ME: Einstein said time was **relative**, right? Maybe **I'm not late**. Maybe **you guys are early**.

Guess who didn't laugh? Right, Ms Calleros.

I've got to learn not to talk so much and just do physics.

Ms Calleros really has my number.

She **knows** that I'm having a hard time adjusting to the new school and that **I sort of don't really want to be here,** even though **I'm trying.**

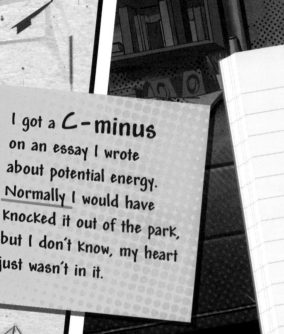

I got a **C-minus** on an essay I wrote about potential energy. <u>Normally</u> I would have knocked it out of the park, but I don't know, my heart just wasn't in it.

Ms Calleros was cool, though. She let me rewrite the essay. **Need more teachers like her.**

C-

Potential Energy Essay

Miles Morales

$$P.E. = m \times g \times h$$

m: mass

g: Gravitational Accela

(9.8 m/s

h: Height

One pretty awesome thing
we watched in Ms Calleros' class
was a documentary
on **Multiverse Theory.**

The director of Alchemax Laboratories was trying to explain the thinking behind it and I was **fascinated.** Not so sure about the other kids in class.

I'll write more about this later, because I have a feeling it's going to have a big impact on my life.

$N = R_* \cdot f_p \cdot n_e \cdot f_l \cdot f_i \cdot f_c \cdot L$

I think one of the **biggest** changes of going to Visions is actually living on campus.

Work is life now!

When I went to Brooklyn Middle, it was just like any other school – y'know, you go to class and you come home.

SPIDER-MAN

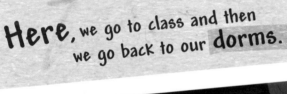

Here, we go to class and then we go back to our dorms.

My room is okay, I guess. Even if I do have a roommate who doesn't really talk to me.

So if I don't want to **not talk** to my roommate and I don't have class, I can always take advantage of one of the lab spaces.

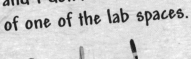

They're really high-tech,

like something out of a movie.

Every kind of equipment you could ask for!

It's like playing with the **world's biggest, best Lego set.**

I wonder what I might come up with in a place like this?

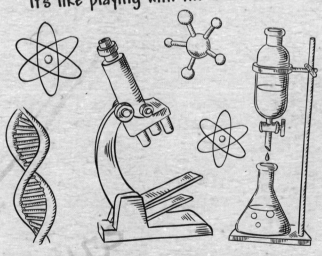

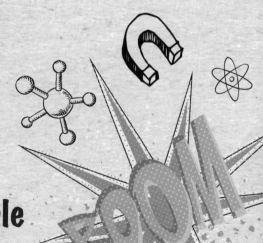

Or what kind of trouble I might get into...!

One thing I remember my mum telling me about before my first day at Visions was the reading.

"There might be a **little more** reading than you'd usually have at Brooklyn Middle,"

she said.

Man, she wasn't joking.

First day there, I got hit! **Book** after **book** and at least a chapter from each every night.

(And) we have to remember it all!

In case you wondered, THAT'S the sound I make
when I'm bitten by a weird glowing spider!

That night totally **changed my life.**

I'm going write it all down, so I don't forget.

Not that I ever could.

AAAAHHHH!!!!!

In case you wondered, THAT'S the sound I make when I'm bitten by a weird glowing spider!

That night totally **changed my life.**

I'm going write it all down, so I don't forget.

Not that I ever could.

I was **so busy** painting with my Uncle Aaron,
I didn't even notice the spider.
I was in the zone.
Just listening to music,
I was lost in the art.
Guess that spider was lost, too.

Something had happened to it. The way it was glowing...
If I had seen it, I'm **sure** I would have jumped
and none of this ever would have happened.

But I didn't **see** it.

It, however ...

saw me.

I **freaked out** when the thing bit me. I felt kind of **weird** after. Started sweating a lot, for one thing. When I got back to the dorms that night, I jumped into bed and passed out.

But when I woke up in the morning, that's when I really started to notice that something was different. Like, my school uniform was too short. I thought

"Miles, did you shrink your school uniform?"

But then I remembered that I don't do my own washing precisely so I DON'T accidentally shrink anything. So then I thought,

"Miles, are you going through puberty?"

But that wasn't it, either.

That's weird...
My school uniform
has shrunk.

So far, so weird. Then I ran into Wanda.

I've already told you about this.

Put my hand on her shoulder,
stuck to her, blah blah blah.

But you know how it is.
You're a kid, you've got a lot on your mind,

you're busy sticking to people.

Continued...

Oh, and remember the security guard, the one whose office I ran into by accident? Well, he was chasing me, so I got in there and slammed the door.

Next thing I knew, I found myself sticking to EVERYTHIN

Even the **walls!** I started to go right up `em.

Good thing I rolled out of the window **before** anyone saw me.

Not that I INTENDED to roll out of the window.

That night, I went back down to the subway tunnel, to find the spider.

Sure enough, **it was glowing.** I don't know if you know this or not, but spiders don't usually glow. **Like, ever.**

Things got even stranger when I looked down an abandoned tunnel and saw the word ALCHEMAX stamped on it. Not sure what business they would have messing around in the subway tunnels. But I didn't have any time to think about it. I had this really uneasy feeling, like something was telling me to **MOVE IT!** So I did and a second later, a subway car smashed right into the wall.

I think that 'uneasy' feeling was warning me of danger, something I got from the spider!

Along with some crazy reflexes that let me jump out of the way.

Things were moving **SO** fast that it took a minute to register what was going on.

There I was, caught between **Spider-Man** and the **Green Goblin** – on a school night!

Never in a **million years** did I think **I'd** ever meet Spider-Man.

I think that's when it really hit me – I had spider powers, too, just like him! Well, maybe not **JUST** like him.

But probably just **like** him.

Y'know, I don't know.

There's probably more to it than that, **biologically speaking,**

but that's essentially what happens.

If I hit someone, they're pretty much out of it for a while.

It's going to take some time to get used to this.

One thing I did work out right away
was that I was going to need a **costume**.
Sure, there was the classic Spider-Man look.

But maybe I could try something **different** ...

something **bold** ...

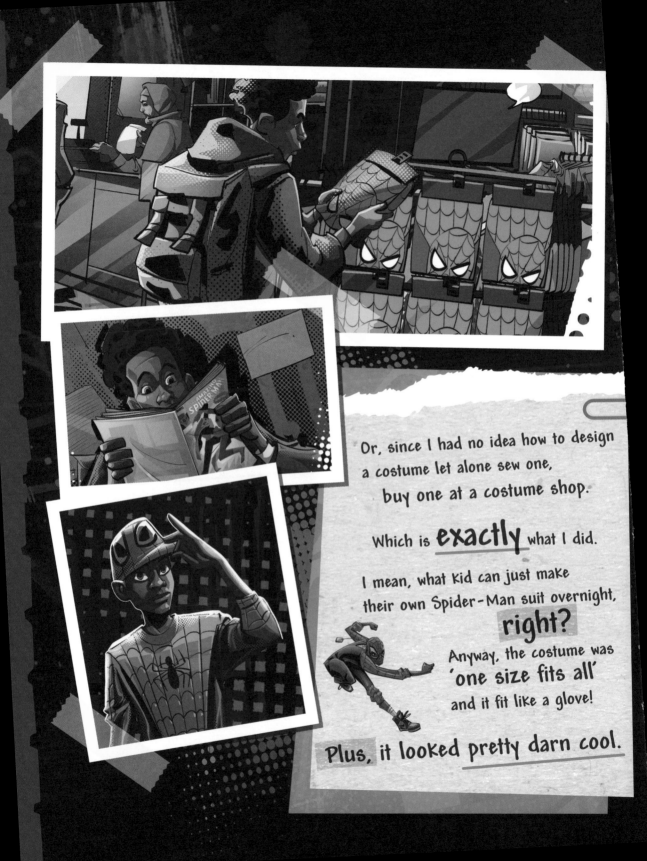

Or, since I had no idea how to design a costume let alone sew one, buy one at a costume shop.

Which is **exactly** what I did.

I mean, what kid can just make their own Spider-Man suit overnight, **right?**

Anyway, the costume was 'one size fits all' and it fit like a glove!

Plus, it looked pretty darn cool.

No way you can predict how life is going to turn out.

I gained some pretty **amazing powers**.

But like a guy once said, that meant I was going to have some pretty amazing **responsibilities**, too.

So who was going to teach me about that?

You'll never guess.*

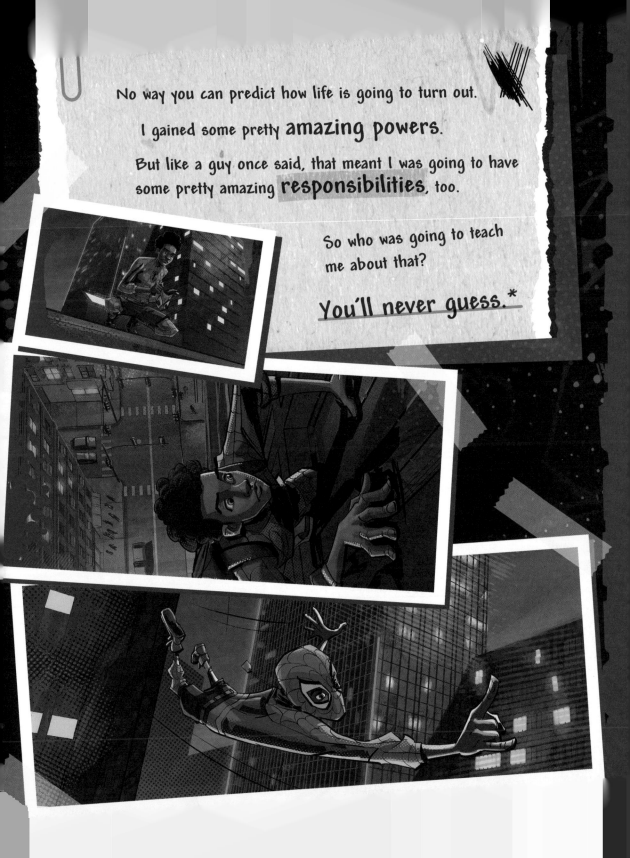

PETER PARKERS

Spider-Man is really **Peter Parker.**

Actually, there's more than one Spider-Man.

And more than one Peter Parker.

Boy, this really is confusing.

Let me try to explain it all as clearly as I can. Because I'm not sure that even I understand it!

The first Spider-Man I met was a guy named Peter Parker.

He was older than me, but not, like, **really old**.

Maybe like 27 or so.

He was fighting the Green Goblin, a 25-foot-tall dude **with wings**.

Peter knew he had to stop the Goblin and he did.

Peter was the first one who knew exactly what had happened to me and what I had become.

Then I met **another Peter Parker.**
From a different universe.

But more on that later.

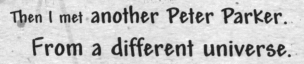

This Peter Parker was older
than the first one I met.

He was also Spider-Man.

He'd been doing that job
for years in his own universe,
before he got sucked into some
crazy, psychedelic portal
and arrived in my world.

Peter knew all the
ins and outs
of being a Super Hero.

So if anyone could teach me
how to be a wall-crawling,
web-spinning good guy,
it was **definitely him.**

At first I couldn't work out **why** there were **two Peter Parkers.**

So I did what you do when you don't know what's going on.

You tie a guy to a chair and **get some answers.**

Peter told me what he thought was going on and I **totally** guessed that he came from a different universe.

Go, me!

I asked Peter to teach me how to be Spider-Man and he agreed. He had a whole load of lessons.

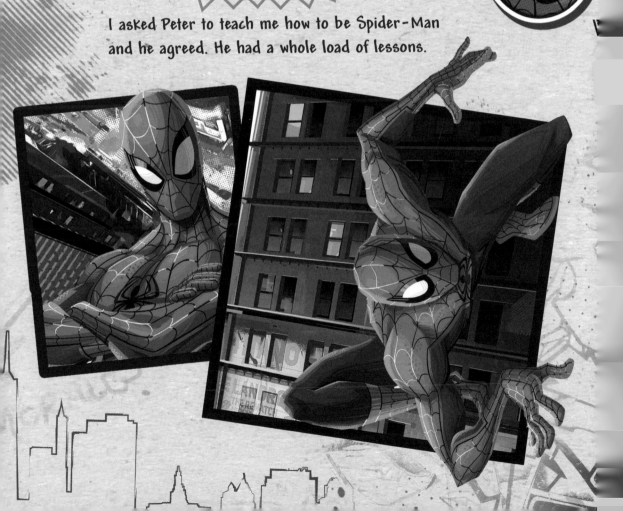

First lesson?

"Don't watch the mouth. Watch the hands."

DON'T WATCH

Turns out the whole time I was listening to Peter talk, he was busy untying himself. Got to remember that one.

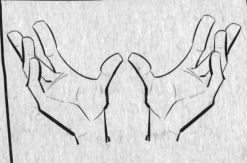

WATCH

 # Second lesson?

"Don't be a fool, stay in school."

This he told me right after he kicked a chair at me and webbed my mouth shut. Turns out, he didn't really want to help me learn to be Spider-Man. He just wanted to get back to his own universe.

Then he tried to leave, but **something happened.**

It was like he glitched –

like his body didn't like being away from his own universe.

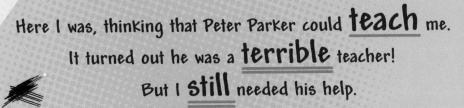

Here I was, thinking that Peter Parker could **teach** me.
It turned out he was a **terrible** teacher!
But I **still** needed his help.

A bad guy called the Kingpin had developed this super collider.
He'd already used it at least once and Peter was pretty sure
that's what opened the portal that brought him to my world.
But it also caused a **massive** earthquake here.

If the Kingpin used it again,
it would **destroy** Brooklyn.
Bye bye Mum, bye bye Dad,
bye bye EVERYONE.

It took a lot, but I **finally** convinced Peter to stay.
Even if he kind of thought that it was his own idea.

REALLY?!?

I guess the third lesson was,

"Watch Peter eat before doing anything else."

It turned out that in Peter's universe, this burger joint had closed six years ago. So he insisted on getting a burger before any further lessons. Here are a couple of pro tips he gave me in between bites:

* Disinfect the mask
* Put baby powder in the suit to avoid <u>chafing</u>

Yeah, he was a baaaaaaad teacher.

But I started to come around.
I had this insane idea that I would wear
a yellow cape with my costume.

L.O.L

I thought it looked cool.

In retrospect, I'm sure it didn't.

But Peter?

He knew it looked awful right away. "It's a 'no' on the cape!"

he said and he yanked it right off.

Then he blew his
nose on it

SPIDER-MAN

I had a lot to learn about being Spider-Man, apparently.

Even though I thought that this Peter Parker wasn't **the best**, it turned out that he really could teach me a lot. Like how to remain **calm** under pressure. We were hacking into Alchemax's computer mainframe when the Kingpin showed up. Instead of **freaking out** (like I was doing!), Peter was cool as a cucumber. ⟶

We kept a low profile, got what we needed, then we were **out of there**.

And **then** I learned that I could turn invisible.

"I'm invisible! **Get it?**"

A LESSON PETER **DID NOT** TEACH ME!!!

It was a **bumpy ride,**
but the more I hung out with Peter,
the more I realized that he had
the Spider-Man thing **down**.

I was all concerned about learning how
to crawl up walls and swing on webs.

But he taught me that there's other stuff that's just as important –

maybe **more important**.

Because it doesn't matter what powers you've got*.

What matters is what do you do with 'em.

*Okay, it matters a little.

Multiverse Theory and You!

I'm still trying to wrap my head around Multiverse Theory.
It's kind of mind blowing!

If you sit down and try to explain it to somebody (like Mum), they sort of look at you like you have four extra arms or something.

But I think if I write it all down, it'll start to make some sense.

At least, I hope it will!

We watched this documentary about Multiverse Theory in Ms Calleros' class. The director of Alchemax Laboratories explained it kind of like this:

Every choice we make could create countless other possibilities, a 'What If' to infinity. That's the Multiverse.

Huh?

Okay, what I think it really means is this.
Say you're making an important decision,
like what to have for breakfast.

Pick one:

 CEREAL   BACON AND EGGS

Congratulations! There are now TWO realities:

One, where you had cereal for breakfast. The other, where you had bacon and eggs. So somewhere out there, different worlds – universes – exist, similar to our own, but with many, many differences.

Or, to put it another way, here's what I said when
I tried to work out how I could **possibly** meet
<u>**two Peter Parkers:**</u>

"Are you from **another** dimension?
Like a parallel universe where things
are like this universe, but different?
And you're Spider-Man in that
universe and you somehow travelled
to this universe?"

Peter **knew** what I was talking about.

Of course he **knew**
what I was talking about.

He's
Spider-Man!

Just so you can see, this is my brain.

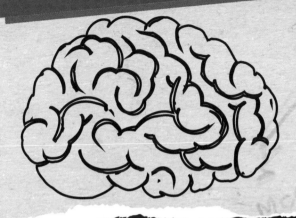

This is my brain on Multiverse Theory.

BOOOM

IT'S NUTS.

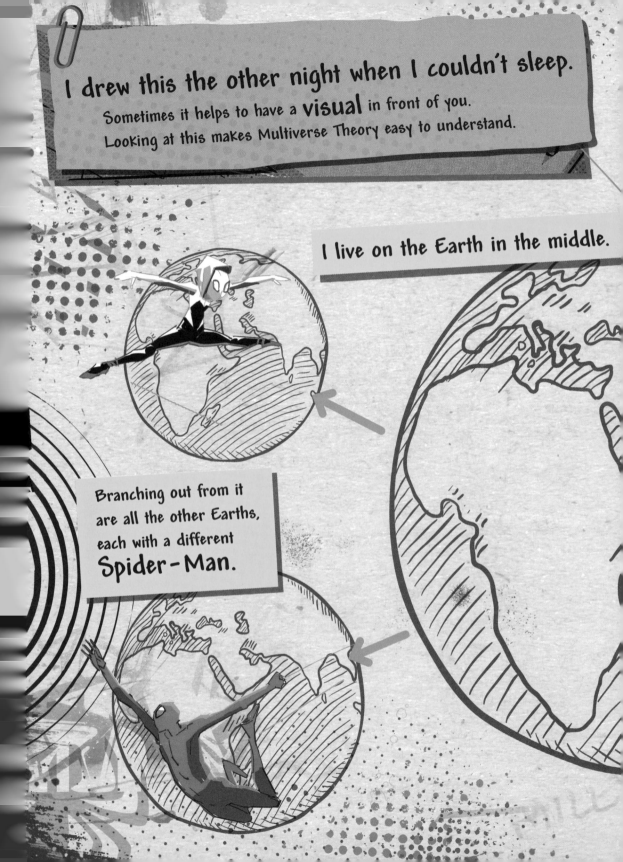

I drew this the other night when I couldn't sleep.
Sometimes it helps to have a **visual** in front of you.
Looking at this makes Multiverse Theory easy to understand.

I live on the Earth in the middle.

Branching out from it are all the other Earths, each with a different **Spider-Man.**

I've already met a load of them
and I'll write about 'em later.

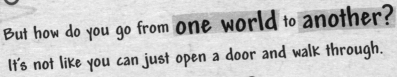

But how do you go from **one world** to **another?**

It's not like you can just open a door and walk through.

Or can you?

The Kingpin thought so. He forced scientists to build a super collider that could harness energy and open a rift between parallel worlds, allowing things to move back and forth between them.

If it sounds messy and dangerous, that's because it is.

I think I mentioned the earthquakes it caused before. **Bad stuff.**

Turns out there are some physical side effects to moving between worlds, too.

Peter experienced them right after he came to my world. He'd be fine one minute, then ZAP! His powers would cut out and he'd fall, then he'd quickly recover.

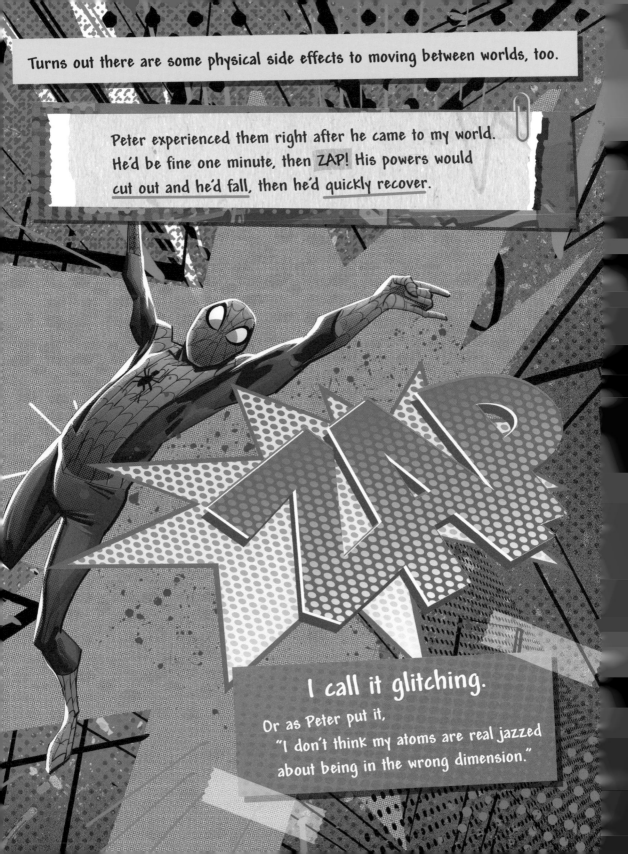

I call it glitching.

Or as Peter put it, "I don't think my atoms are real jazzed about being in the wrong dimension."

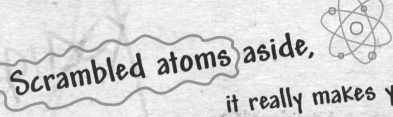

Scrambled atoms aside,

it really makes you stop to think

...hile you're doing something in your world, at that **exact moment** something similar but completely different could be happening to 'you' in countless other worlds.

Since I met Peter(s),
I've met a few spiders from different worlds.
One of those worlds I call Earth-14512
(yeah, I numbered 'em – makes it easier to keep track of it all).
On that one, there's **no Spider-Man** like I know.

It's kind of a robot, called SP//dr,

and a kid named Peni Parker.

And then there's Earth-90214.

It's a pretty strange place – the world is actually **black and white!**

I'm not talking about the morality. I'm talking about the colour –

literally **everything** is shades of black and white.

Not sure how the science of all that works.

I should ask Ms Calleros sometime...

Last but not least, there's Earth-8311.

I don't even know where to begin.

The Spider-Man from that world is a ...

well, he's a pig.

But not like a 'run-around-on-all-fours' pig.

You know what? I'll explain later.

Anyway,

that world is about as different from mine as you can possibly get.

Spiders! SPIDERS! SPIDERS!!!!!!!!!!

I added lots of exclamation marks because I thought it would make this page seem really exciting. It Kind of does. So yeah, spiders!

There sure are a lot of them. At first, like everyone else, I thought there was just the one Spider-Man. But I was proven wrong pretty quickly. Not only did I meet a second Spider-Man, but then I started to meet different spider people from different worlds.

And not only people, pigs!

A talking pig! Freaky!

Yeah, so ... a talking pig.

It took a little getting used to,
y'know, having a conversation with a hog.

But Spider-Ham (can't believe I have to call him that)
was just as heroic as the other spiders.

Turns out, he had a pretty strange origin.

He used to be a plain, ordinary spider
who was bitten by a radioactive pig.

The bite transformed that little spider into an awesome pig with spider powers, who decided to put on a costume and fight crime.

He's got a little bit of an attitude, but I kind of like that.
I'm a Brooklyn kid, we all have attitude!

Spider-Gwen's about as <u>different</u> from a talking pig as you can get. She's <u>really</u> a kid named **Gwen Stacy** and she's 15 - not much older than me.

She got her **spider powers** from the bite of a radioactive spider

(I see a theme developing...).

In her world, Peter Parker turned into some kind of **lizard creature** or something?

Oh, and she's a dead ringer for **Wanda!**

Man, this Multiverse stuff is a trip.

Now THIS guy is serious.

Sooooooo serious.

Makes me glad we had a talking pig around to lighten the mood.

I already told you a little about his world, all black and white?

Yeah, weird.

Anyway.

He was bitten by a **non**-radioactive spider that came out of an antique spider statue.

creepy.

The bite gave him what I call

'the standard Spider-Man powers'.

Then he used them to fight the Goblin in his world, along with a creepy dude called the Vulture.

Okay,  now this kid's cool!

She was bitten by a radioactive spider, but she didn't get **the standard Spider-Man powers**.

Instead, the spider bite **forged a bond** between her and the spider.

And together, they were able to pilot something called the SP//dr suit – a kind of robot Spider-Man (it even has web-shooters!) made by her father.

That SP//dr can do all the stuff that the spider people can do.

Plus, IT'S A ROBOT.

Now, you may think that hanging out with a whole bunch of spider people (and pig) would be **awesome**. And you'd be right!

SPIDER-MAN (PETER PARKER): Cracking jokes while fighting helps you relax. But avoid the potty humour. You're better than that.

SPIDER-GWEN: You need to learn about maintaining control of your abilities.

SPIDER-MAN NOIR: Punch, punch, kick, punch, head fake, head fake, head fake...

SPIDER-MAN

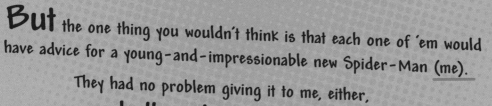

But the one thing you wouldn't think is that each one of 'em would have advice for a young-and-impressionable new Spider-Man (me).

They had no problem giving it to me, either,

and all at the same time.

Too bad that spider bite didn't give me spider hearing!*

SPIDER-HAM:

Disinfect the mask.
Trust me. I'm a pig.

PENI PARKER: Let me tell you a thing or thirty about electrical engineering...

*Is that a thing?

Not sure if that's a thing.

Probably not a thing.

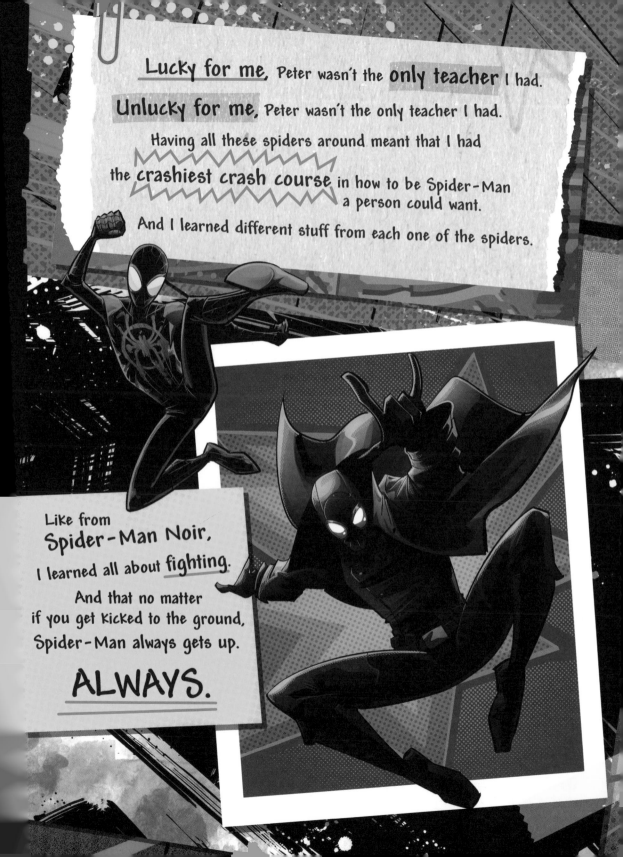

Lucky for me, Peter wasn't the **only teacher** I had.

Unlucky for me, Peter wasn't the only teacher I had.

Having all these spiders around meant that I had

the crashiest crash course in how to be Spider-Man a person could want.

And I learned different stuff from each one of the spiders.

Like from **Spider-Man Noir,** I learned all about fighting.

And that no matter if you get kicked to the ground, Spider-Man always gets up.

ALWAYS.

And even though Peter likes to joke around (which isn't always funny), he had some **really** good advice for me.

He said,

"**Every** spider person in **every** dimension has faced a test, and we've all come through. You can't just run away when it gets hard."

Sometimes I wish I could just run away. But I know Peter's right. Spider-Man can't just quit. He has to be there. Especially when it counts. Because it always counts.

I had, like, **eight hours** to learn how to be Spider-Man.

All these other spiders had <u>years</u>.

But I had something they didn't have - <u>**them.**</u>

I got a little something from each one,
and after a while, something just ... **clicked.**

It's like I got it.

And maybe it's because we're **all** spiders, we're all linked through the Multiverse, but, **we** just clicked, too.

Bring us together, there's no telling what we can do!

Well, I'll tell you one thing we could do. We were having a **big** meeting in my dorm room and Ganke walked in on us.

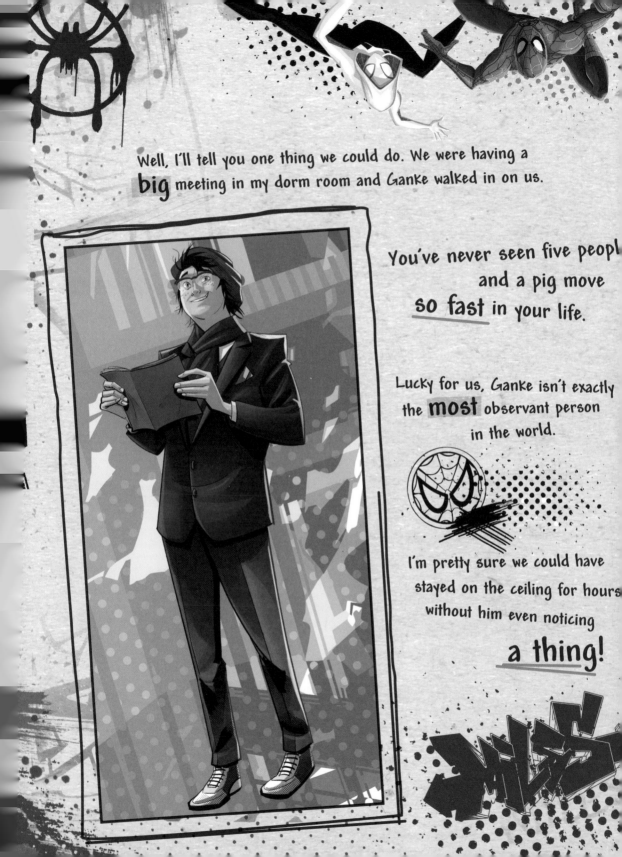

You've never seen five peopl[e] and a pig move **so fast** in your life.

Lucky for us, Ganke isn't exactly the **most** observant person in the world.

I'm pretty sure we could have stayed on the ceiling for hours without him even noticing **a thing!**

SUPER VILLAINS?
More Like Super Annoyances

Someone told me there's an old saying,
that a hero is only as good as their villain.

I wish that saying wasn't true, because it would mean that I get hit **a lot** less.
I've only been Spider-Man for a little while,
but I've already faced off against some pretty **tough** Super Villains.

First up are your garden variety thugs. Just punks, really.

Guys who lend their muscle to make money.

In this town, most of the thugs work for the Kingpin.

They don't have any powers -

like, they're not going to shoot blasts out of their eyes

or paralyze anyone with a six-foot-long poison tongue.

But they do make things more difficult

and can wear you down before you face off

against one of the REALLY bad guys.

I have a few tips on taking down thugs, which,

strangely enough, spell out the word

'THUG':

T - Take 'em down fast!

H - Hurt 'em if you have to!

U - Unless you don't!

G - Go home when you've finished!

Okay. I admit it. I just made that up for the journal.

Okay, now I would put this guy in the 'thug' class,
except that he's a **step above a thug.**
I don't know what the word is for that, but he's definitely it.

This guy works for the **Kingpin**
and will do **anything** he asks, without question.
He's got pasty white skin and **creepy pointed teeth.**
Super-strong, **Tombstone** can also take a beating –
like, I've seen Spider-Man punch him right in the face
and it's as though that guy **doesn't even feel it.**

The Scorpion is another guy who's kind of like a thug, but isn't a thug, because he's got some serious powers.

Like Tombstone, he works for **the Kingpin.**

Unlike Tombstone, he has a set of **scorpion-like powers** (I guess that accounts for the name) – mainly **super-strength.**

He wears a heavy-duty suit of armour, with a tail attached to it.

That tail is deadly!

It can smash stuff and it can spray acid, too.

Pretty sure a regular scorpion **can't** do that, but what do I know.*

*I know a lot, I'm super-smart!

Q: Is every villain in this city employed by Kingpin?

A: Yes!
Well, maybe not every villain, but it sure seems that way.

The Green Goblin also worked for the Kingpin, but it's pretty hard to imagine that a guy like that would work for anybody.

First of all, the Goblin had to be about 25-feet tall, easy. On his back, he had these two huge wings and he could flap 'em and fly anywhere. And he had this crazy long blue tongue.

Did I mention that he was super-strong, too? Yeah, he was super-strong, too.

I never had to fight him. I watched Spider-Man* take him on, though. He nearly beat the web-head. Ugh, the less I think about that the better.

*The first Peter Parker I met, not the second one.

The **Prowler** not only works for the Kingpin (surprise!), but he's also kind of like his **right-hand man.** Also his left-hand man. Maybe even his feet, too. The Prowler is like the go-to guy, the one who can always get the job done. Of course, **every job** is a dirty one for this guy. He's really strong and has these **gauntlets** that he wears that can **blast** at unsuspecting spiders.

And here we have the **ultimate bad guy**, the main man who's in charge of all that's wrong in New York City.

The Kingpin. His real name is Wilson Fisk, the man behind Fisk Industries, one of the most powerful corporations **in the world.**

Most people think Fisk is just a rich dude who donates money to hospitals and zoos*. But the few heroes who have uncovered his real identity know that Fisk controls almost **all of the crime in New York.**

Which doesn't explain why he's using a super collider to bridge the gap between the different worlds in the Multiverse.

What's his game? **Why** is he doing it? Only Kingpin **knows** ...

but I'm going to find out.

*I don't know for sure if he donates money to zoos. That's just a guess.

Just wanted to write down a **few** observations on each of these bad guys. Not like I won't remember them forever!

TOMBSTONE

Knows how to throw a punch.
Hurts when you hit his skin –
it's hard!
Nice hair, though.

SCORPION

Watch out for the tail.
Repeat – watch out for the tail!
Acid = no fun.

GREEN GOBLIN

Tongue = gross!
How'd he get so tall?

PROWLER

Costume looks cool, for a bad guy.
Seems really familiar ...
do I know him?

KINGPIN

For someone **so big.**
he moves really fast!
And he knows how to hit!

I still can't believe everything that's happened to me.

I went from **zero** to battling **Super Villains** in one day.

From never having been in a fight in my life to fighting **for my life.**

It all seems like a **dream** sometimes ...

or a pretty nasty nightmare!

And I can't believe I'm at the end of this journal **already** -

when my career as Spider-Man has only **just started!**

I'll have to get another notebook,
so that I can keep writing.

I have no idea

what the future holds,
but I'm **sure** of one thing -

it won't be boring!

ILES MORALES

	MONDAY	TUESDAY	WEDNESDAY
7:30-9:00am	Social Science	Introduction to Literature	Social Science
9:05-10:25am	Trigonometry	Computer Science	Trigonometry
10:30-11:25am	Advanced Physics	Study	Advanced Physics
11:30am-12:00pm	Lunch	Lunch	Lunch
12:05-1:30pm	Anatomy & Physiology	Physical Education	Anatomy & Physiology
1:35-3:00pm	History	Advanced Physics Lab	History
4:00pm-12:00am			STUDY!!!
12:00-7:25am	Sleep?	Sleep would be good	Seriously, sleep

VISIONS